VOL. 7

HAL•LEONARD® KEYBOARD PLAY-ALONG

POP/ROCK Classics

CW00406711

CONTENTS

Page	Title	Demo Track	Play-Along Track
2	Baba O'Riley THE WHO	1	9
12	Bloody Well Right SUPERTRAMP	2	10
18	Changes DAVID BOWIE	3	11
24	Cold As Ice FOREIGNER	4	12
31	Don't Know Much LINDA RONSTADT & AARON NEVILLE	5	13
36	I Write The Songs BARRY MANILOW	6	14
42	That's All GENESIS	7	15
50	We've Only Just Begun CARPENTERS	8	16

Exclusive Distributors:
Music Sales Limited
14-15 Berners Street, London W1T 3LJ, UK.

Order No. HLE90003683
ISBN: 978-1-84772-789-3
This book © Copyright 2008 Hal Leonard Europe

www.musicsales.com

This publication is not authorised for sale in
the United States of America and/or Canada

HAL LEONARD EUROPE
DISTRIBUTED BY MUSIC SALES

Baba O'Riley

Words and Music by
Peter Townshend

Moderately (♩ = 120)

Play 11 times

Play 6 times

Play 7 times

*Sequenced keyboard arranged for piano.

Play 4 times

f

With pedal

Out here ___ in the fields, ___   I fight ___ for my meals. ___
I don't ___ need to fight ___   to prove _____ I'm right. ___

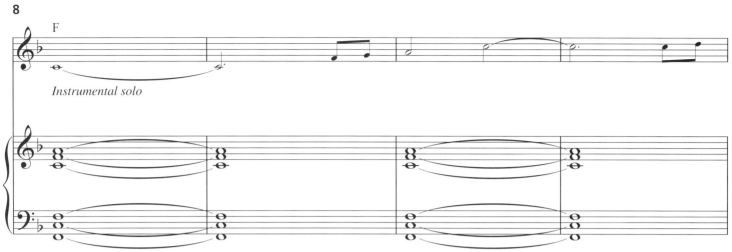

Instrumental solo

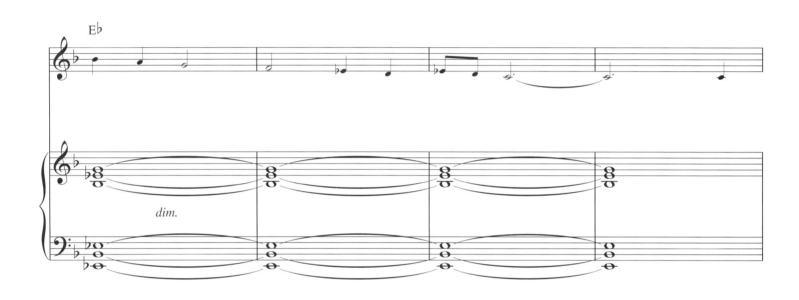

cresc. poco a poco

Bass

(Piano)

(Instrumental solo continues)

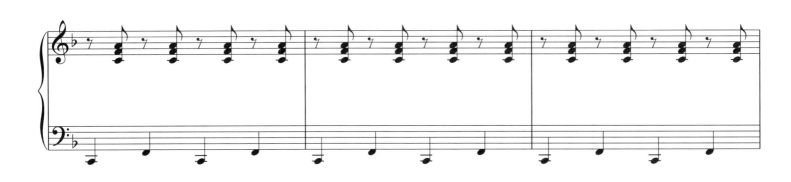

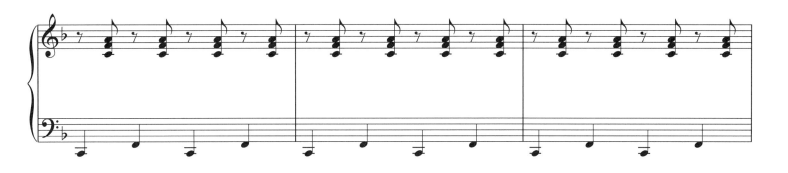

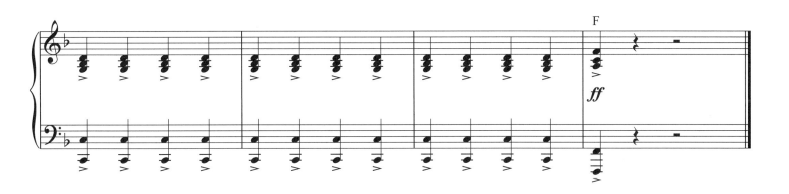

Bloody Well Right

Words and Music by Rick Davies
and Roger Hodgson

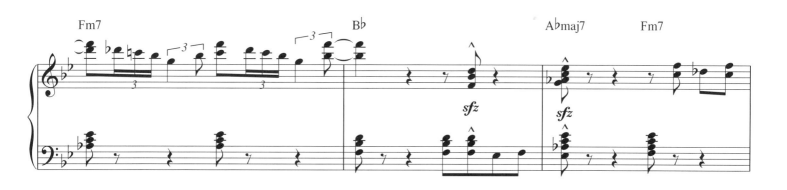

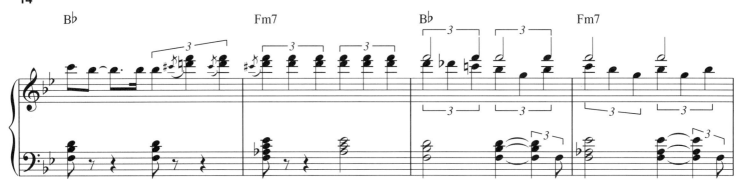

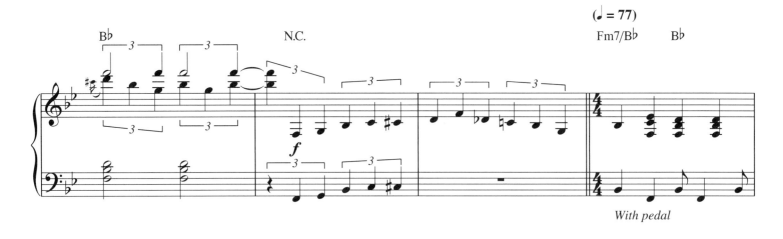

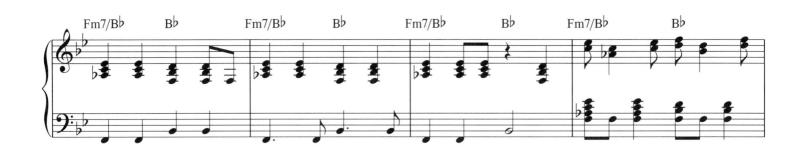

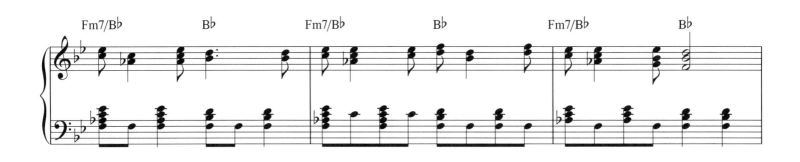

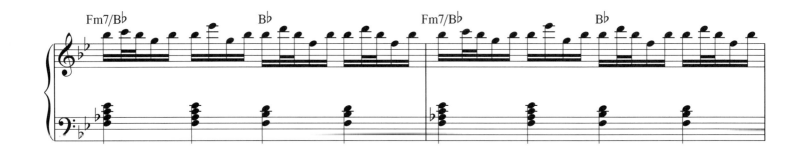

So   you think _ your _ school-ing's phon-y,
Write   your prob - lems _ down   in   de - tail

I   guess   it's   hard   not   to   a - gree. _____
and   take   them   to   a   high - er   place. _____

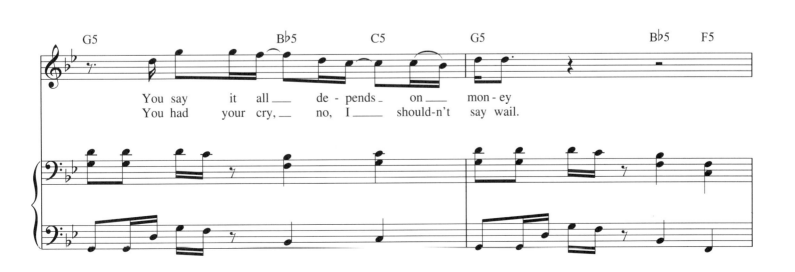

You   say   it   all ___ de - pends _ on ___ mon - ey
You   had   your   cry, _   no,   I _____ should-n't   say   wail.

Changes

Words and Music by
David Bowie

Still don't know what I ___ was wait - ing for ___ and my
I watch the rip - ples change their size ___ but

time was run - ning wild. ___ A mil - lion dead - end streets ___ and ev - 'ry time I thought I'd
never leave the stream ___ of warm im - per - ma - nence, ___ and so the days ___ flow

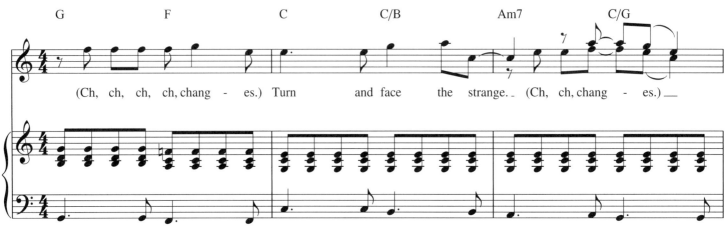

Cold As Ice

Words and Music by Mick Jones
and Lou Gramm

You're as cold ___ as ice,

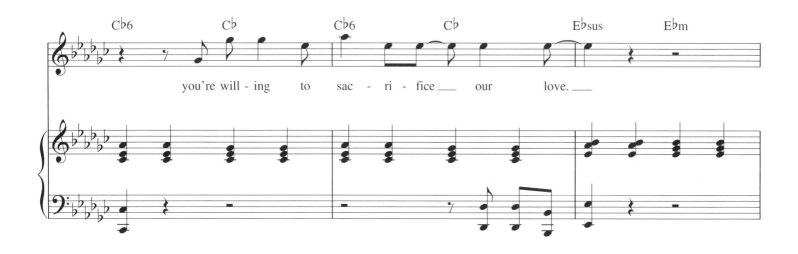

you're will-ing to sac-ri-fice ___ our love. ___

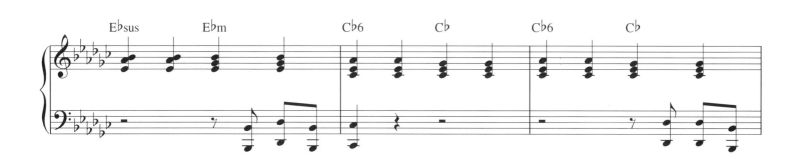

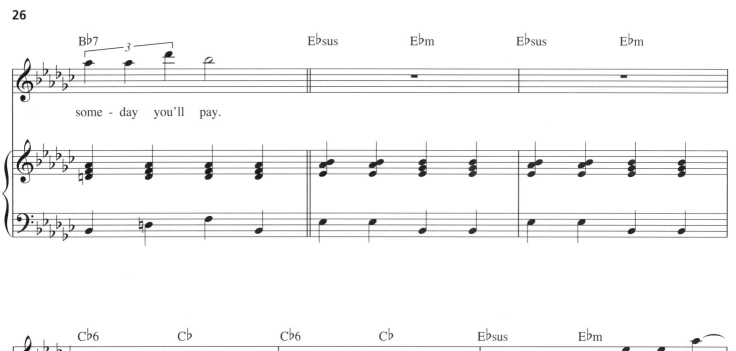

some - day you'll pay.

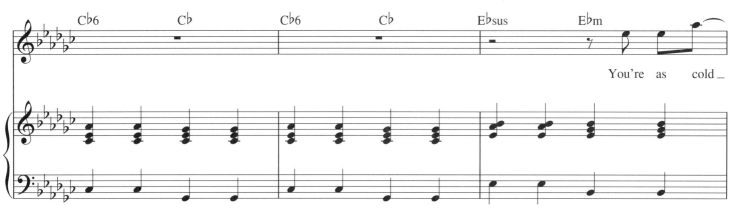

You're as cold __

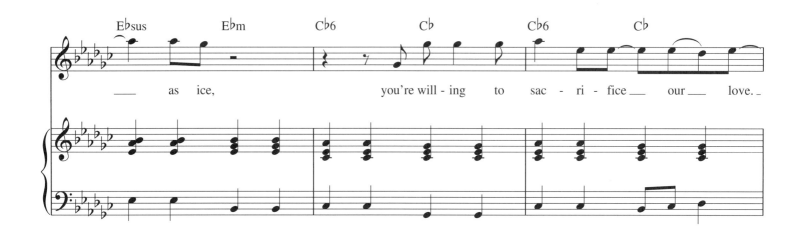

__ as ice, you're will - ing to sac - ri - fice __ our __ love. __

throw-ing a - way ___ a for-tune in feel - ings ___ must some-day you'll pay. ___

(Cold

With pedal

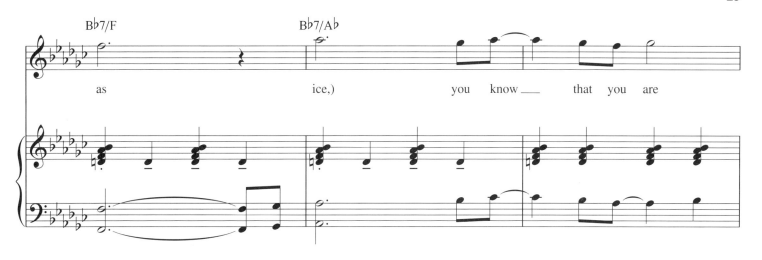

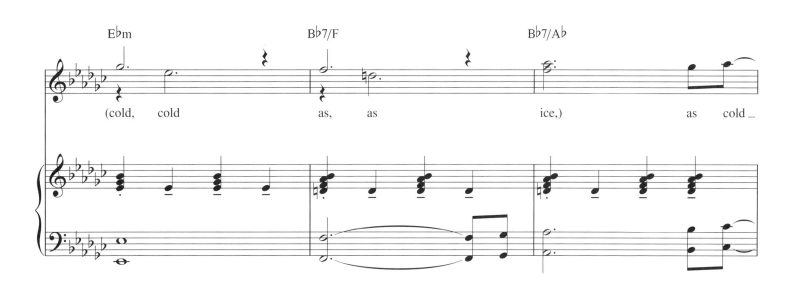

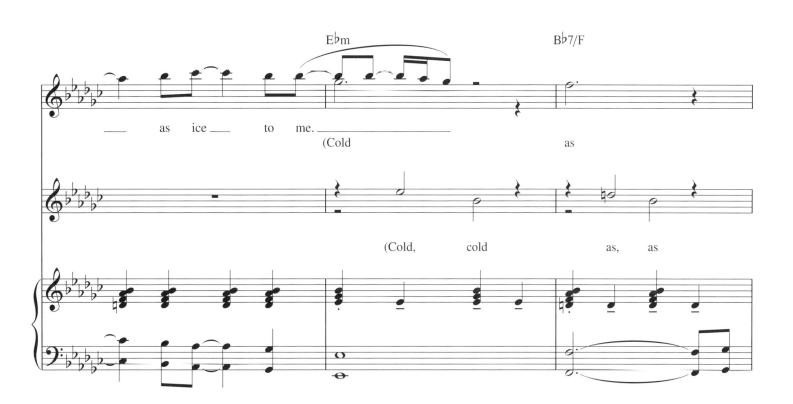

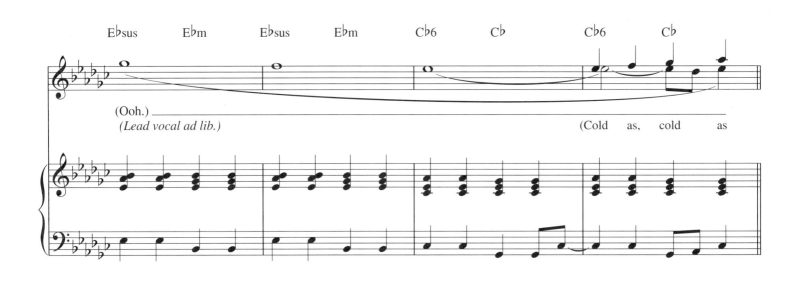

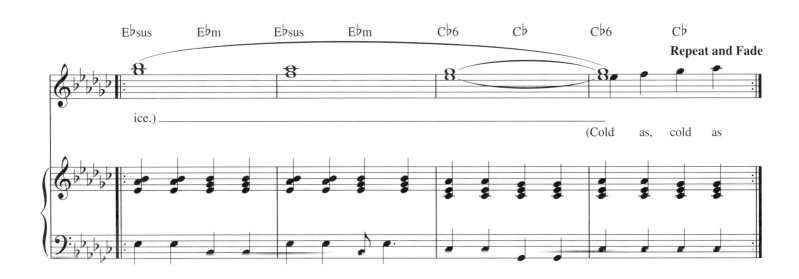

Don't Know Much

Words and Music by Barry Mann,
Cynthia Weil and Tom Snow

I Write The Songs

Words and Music by
Bruce Johnston

That's All

Words and Music by Tony Banks,
Phil Collins and Mike Rutherford

Moderately slow (♩ = 88)

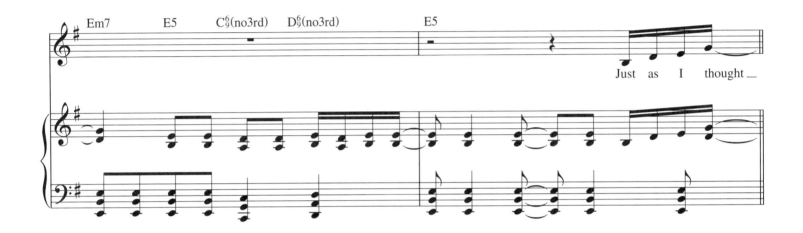

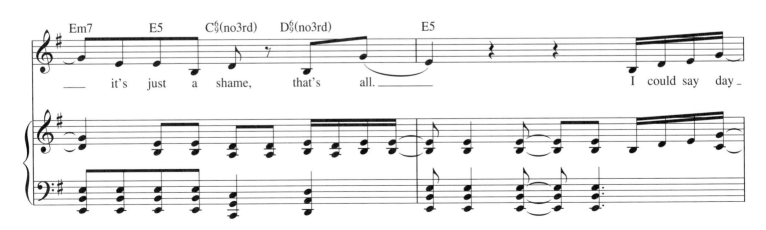

To Coda ⊕

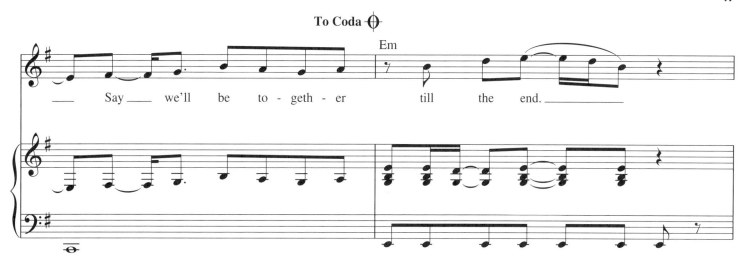

Say __ we'll be to - geth - er till the end. ___

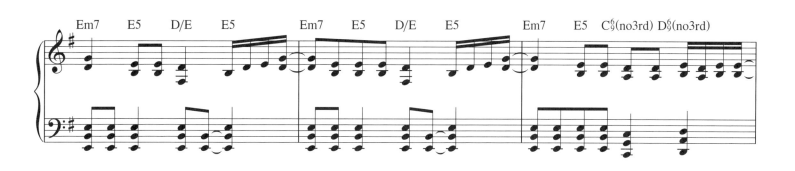

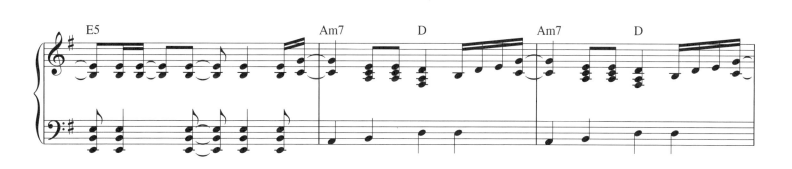

D.S. al Coda

But I could

That's all.

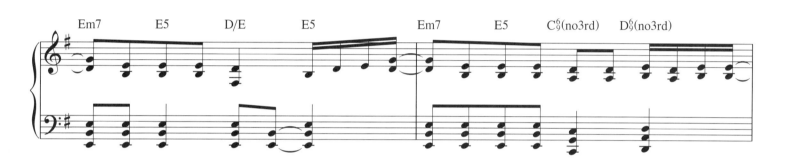

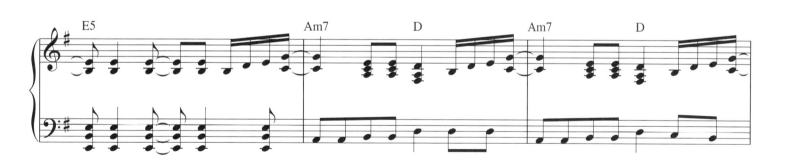

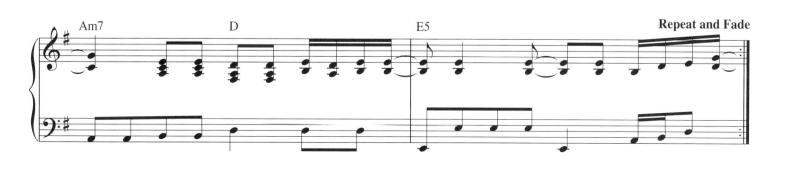

We've Only Just Begun

Words and Music by Roger Nichols
and Paul Williams

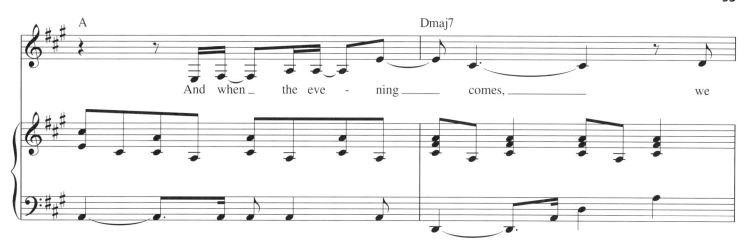

And when _ the eve - ning _____ comes, _____ we

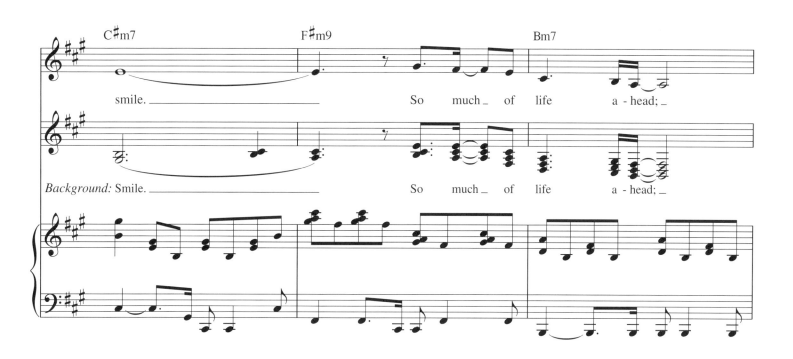

smile. _____ So much _ of life a - head; _

Background: Smile. _____ So much _ of life a - head; _

we'll find a place _ where there's room to grow, _____

we'll find a place _ where there's room to grow, _____

we'll find a place _ where there's room to grow,

we'll find a place _ where there's room to grow,

and yes, we've just be - gun. _____